Magic Mates

and the
Moody Monday

Ja<del>n</del>e West

<del>Ill</del>ustrated by

Stik

<del>KINGFISHER</del> STARS

Rising Stars UK Ltd.
22 Grafton Street, London W1S 4EX
www.risingstars-uk.com

The right of Jane West to be identified as the author of this work
has been asserted by her in accordance with the Copyright, Design
and Patents Act 1988.

Published 2008

Cover design: Button plc
Illustrator: Stik, Bill Greenhead for Illustration
Text design and typesetting: Andy Wilson
Publisher: Gill Budgell
Editor: Jane Wood

British Library Cataloguing in Publication Data.
A CIP record for this book is available from the British Library

ISBN: 978-1-84680-328-4

Printed in the UK by CPI Bookmarque, Croydon, CR0 4TD

Contents

Meet the Magic Mates

The Magic Mates are best friends –
but that doesn't mean they're all alike.

Name: *Izzie*

The sporty one: can climb trees, surf and take on the boys at their own game – and win.

Travels by: running!

Loves: trendy tracksuits, open skies and sandy beaches.

Hates: standing still.

Name: *Meena*

The girly one: uses her mobile for networking and planning her social life.

Travels by: Mum's car (her personal chauffeur).

Loves: pink and her Magic Mates.

Hates: breaking a nail.

Name: 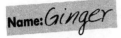Ginger

The ginger one: you don't wanna mess with this feisty gal – the Kung Fu and quick quip queen!

Travels by: push-scooter.

Loves: Jackie Chan and her Magic Mate pals.

Hates: nail extensions.

Name: Jo

The clever one: uses her brains and quick wit to talk her way out of trouble. Sometimes she's a bit too quick.

Travels by: bicycle and is designing a pair of motorised rollerblades.

Loves: Jacqueline Wilson, Cathy Cassidy and Albert Einstein.

Hates: being called 'geek', 'nerd', 'swot' or 'boffin'.

Name: Ellie

The fashion-conscious one: can tell her Prada from her Asda and knows how to accessorise.

Travels by: limousine, of course! (But only in her dreams.)

Loves: shopping.

Hates: anything to do with getting dirty; anyone who upsets her Magic Mates.

Name: Yash

The funky punky one: the 'alternative' one of the gang who hugs trees, people and furry animals.

Travels by: skateboard.

Loves: having a good time.

Hates: bullies.

Tell Me Why
I Don't Like Mondays

It's Monday morning at the start of term.
The Magic Mates are going back
to school. The sky is grey and full
of clouds, the air is chilly and the sun
seems to have gone on holiday.

Ellie   Everything is grey. The sky
            is grey, the pavement is grey
            and school is grey.

Meena   I know what you mean. It makes you feel sort of grey and moody. That's why I always wear pink on a Monday – it cheers me up.

Jo   It's not that bad. The school library has got some new computers with some really great CD-ROMs.

Izzie   And we've got PE today. I love playing netball.

Ginger   Yes, and I really like Miss Peters.
           She lets us play 'pirates'
           in the gym.

Yash   Haven't you heard?
           Miss Peters hurt her leg skiing.
           We've got a new PE teacher
           this term.

Ginger   What's she like?

Yash   No one's seen her yet.

Ellie   I hope she's nice. I don't like
           PE very much. I prefer reading
           fashion magazines.

Meena   Me too.

Ginger   I'd rather run round the field
than read magazines
at breaktime.

Ellie   We know. You're mad!
But we love you anyway!

The Magic Mates get ready
for their PE lesson.
But they're in for
a shock. Their new
PE teacher is a man.

Mr Sterne is very tall, with huge muscles
and a shaved head. The Magic Mates
think he looks really scary.

Meena   They have got to be kidding!
             Is he our new PE teacher?

Ginger   Yes. But I don't think
             you want him to catch you
             talking.

Mr Sterne Good morning, boys and girls.
My name is Mr Sterne and I'll
be taking your PE lessons
for the rest of term. Miss Peters
has hurt her leg, but she'll
be back in school soon. Right!
Let's do our warm-ups!
Fifty push-ups from everyone;
then run ten times round
the school field! Go!

Even Izzie and Ginger, who love PE,
find this hard work. All the Magic Mates
are out of breath – just like the rest
of their class. And this is just the warm-up!

Mr Sterne Come on, come on!
Put some effort into it!
You're all soft! Too much TV,
and too many crisps
and bars of chocolate.
Now do your run!

Jo Run! I can't even walk!

Ellie   I can't stand a whole term
          of Mr Sterne.

Meena   I can't stand a whole lesson
          of him!

2

Biscuits
at Breaktime

The Magic Mates decide to go
to the library at breaktime. The library
has big squashy beanbags where you
can curl up to read your book …
or have a rest!

Meena and Ellie need some biscuits first.
The push-ups and running have made
them very hungry. Miss Price won't allow
biscuits in the library so they go to
their classroom first.

Ellie	I'm so hungry I could eat a whole packet of biscuits.
Meena	I could eat two.
Ellie	I could eat a horse AND two packets of biscuits.
Meena	I could eat an elephant and two packets of biscuits and … oh!

Suddenly the girls realise the classroom isn't empty. Mr Sterne is there.
He's trying to hide something
that looks a bit pink and fluffy in his bag.

Mr Sterne   Er ... hello, girls. I thought everyone had gone to the library.

Ellie   We just came in to get some biscuits from our lunchboxes.

Mr Sterne   Young ladies like you shouldn't
be snacking on biscuits.
You should be eating fresh fruit
like an apple or an orange.
They're packed with Vitamin C
and the natural sugar
gives you energy.

Meena   My biscuits have got raisins
in them.

Mr Sterne   Well, hurry up.
Then go outside and play.

Mr Sterne leaves the room taking his bag
with him.

Ellie   What do you think
he was trying to hide in his bag?

Meena   I don't know. It looked like
something pink and fluffy.

Ellie   Well, it can't be his, can it?
Pink is *so* not his colour.

Meena   Let's follow him and see where
he goes.

The Plot Thickens
(and Widens and Deepens)

The girls follow Mr Sterne. He doesn't
go to the staffroom. He's acting
very strangely, looking over his shoulder
to see if he's being followed. Meena
and Ellie quickly hide. Then Mr Sterne
goes into an empty classroom.

Ellie   What's he doing in there?
That's Mrs Smith's classroom.

Meena   I don't know.

Ellie   Now he's gone in her
store cupboard.

Meena   She won't like that.
Let's wait here and see
what he does next.

But the girls are in for a long wait.
Mr Sterne is talking to someone.
With the door closed, it's hard to hear
what he's saying.

Ellie   We'll have to go inside.

Meena   What if he catches us?

Ellie   Say we've come to borrow
a book.

The girls creep inside the classroom.
They hear Mr Sterne's muffled voice
through the store cupboard door.

Mr Sterne Knit one, purl two.

Ellie What's he saying?

Meena I don't know. It sounds like code.

Mr Sterne Loop the wool round,
then purl two, knit one.

Ellie This is so strange. I know
I've heard that before.
Who is it that says that?

Meena Come on, Ellie. Work it out!
What is he mumbling on about?

Ellie Hah! My granny!

Meena Your what? Or rather, who?

Ellie starts to giggle! She knows exactly
what Mr Sterne is doing – he's knitting!
Just like her grandma does.

In the Cupboard

Ellie tells Meena that Mr Sterne
is knitting. Meena isn't convinced.

Meena He can't be knitting.

Ellie Why not?

Meena Because he's a man.
And a PE teacher.

Ellie So what? Lots of famous
fashion designers are men.

Meena   Yes, you're right. It seems funny
at first, but there's no reason
why not, when you think
about it. But why's he hiding
in a store cupboard?

Suddenly the bell goes. The store
cupboard door bursts open
and Mr Sterne comes out. His face
goes bright red when he sees Ellie
and Meena.

Mr Sterne What are you two girls doing?
Have you been following me?
Have you been spying on me?

Ellie We're really sorry …

Meena … but are you …

Ellie … a fashion designer?

Mr Sterne I see you girls have very sharp
eyes – and ears. No, I'm not
a fashion designer. I'm knitting
a jumper for my wife's birthday.

Ellie Oh! Why were you hiding
in the store cupboard?

Mr Sterne   It's a surprise present.

Meena   But you could knit
in the staffroom.

Mr Sterne blushes even more.
Ellie and Meena are puzzled.
Why would anyone knit in a dark,
stuffy store cupboard?

Mr Sterne   I know it's silly, but
people laugh when I tell them
I like to knit. They think men
shouldn't be interested
in knitting. Especially someone
who looks like me.

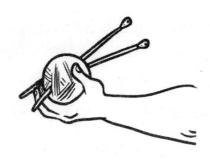

Meena   That's what I thought, at first,
            but I've just realised how silly
            it is. You should be able to do
            whatever you like. It doesn't
            hurt anyone.

Meena   Can we see what you're knitting?

Mr Sterne shows them the jumper
he's making for his wife.

Meena   Oh! It's so pretty!
I love that colour!

Ellie   It's really good!
Knitwear is totally in this season.

Mr Sterne I don't think classic knitwear
ever really dates or goes
out of fashion.

Ellie You're so right!

Meena I wish I could talk to my dad
about fashion.

Ellie Yes, my dad thinks Prada
is the same as Asda.

Mr Sterne It's been fun talking to you, girls.
But we'd all better
get back to our classrooms.

The girls head off for their next class.

Meena   I can't believe how nice he was!
He seemed so mean in PE
this morning.

Ellie   Yes. It's funny how wrong
your first idea of someone
can be.

5

A Knotty Problem

All day Ellie and Meena have been
thinking about Mr Sterne's knitting
problem. They think they've got an idea
that might help him. They go to the
staffroom after school to see him.

Mr Sterne Hello, girls.
Have you come
to discuss
fashion tips?

Ellie	Not exactly.
Meena	But we've had an idea.
Ellie	Why don't you start a school knitting club?
Meena	Then you can teach us to knit – and anyone else who wants to learn.
Mr Sterne	That's a really good idea, girls. Do you think your friends would like to learn to knit, too?

Ellie I'm sure Izzie, Yash, Ginger and Jo will want to learn.

Meena Some of the boys might have a go if *you're* teaching them.

Mr Sterne I'll talk to the headteacher first thing tomorrow.

Meena and Ellie are happy that Mr Sterne thinks a knitting club is a good idea. There's just one more thing they have to say to him.

Ellie Just promise you won't be hiding in the store cupboard again.

Mr Sterne Thanks to you girls, I won't.
I shall do my knitting with pride.
You're right. It's silly to let
people stop you enjoying things.
And talking of letting
people enjoy things –
that's given me an idea, too.

Ellie What sort of idea?

Mr Sterne It's about PE.

Meena (groans)
Oh no, not PE … Oops, sorry!
I forgot that's your lesson!

Mr Sterne Don't worry. That's just
the point! I teach PE because
I really want people to be active
to help them stay healthy.
Now I've realised I need
to let people enjoy what they do,
too. But I didn't help anyone
to enjoy PE this week.
From now on I'm going to show
that PE can be fun, as well
as knitting! That will be better
for all of us!

Meena Now that is what I call
a magic idea!

About the Author

Jane West's mother taught her to knit.
Jane wasn't very good at knitting but
she did make a very long, stripey scarf!

Jane West:

- lives by the beach in Cornwall
- likes taking her dog Pip paddling in the sea
- loves bodyboarding
- has worked in an art gallery, a bookshop and a school.

Now she's a writer, and has had great fun
writing about the Magic Mates. She hopes
you liked reading about them.

Get Knotted!

◎ *The earliest form of knitting is called Nålebinding. It's a word from the country of Denmark, and it means 'binding with a needle'. It was like knitting with one needle, using a series of knots. Nålebinding is thousands and thousands of years old!*

◎ Archaeologists found some knitted socks in Egypt that are over 1000 years old.

◎ *Five hundred years ago, Queen Elizabeth I wore stockings knitted from silk.*

◎ Fair Isle knitting developed in Scotland. It's a way of making colourful patterns with wool.

◎ *During the Second World War, there was such a shortage of wool that people unpicked old jumpers and used the wool to make something new. This was called 'make-do and mend'.*

◎ Famous knitters include: Julia Roberts, Dakota Fanning and Cameron Diaz.

◎ *There are several men-only knitting groups. There's even a website dedicated to men knitters: www.menknit.net.*

◎ Lots of people in the UK like knitting: 4,000,000 women and 448,000 men.

◎ *If you'd like to learn to knit, there are lots of books and websites that can help you:*
www.learn2knit.co.uk
www.knittinghelp.com

Knitting Lingo

Needles   What you use to knit. They're much longer than sewing needles, with blunt ends (and you don't have to thread the wool through them).

Casting on   Starting to knit.

Plain   The most basic stitch. If you can do this (and it's pretty easy), you're knitting!

Purl   Turning the stitch the other way round. This gives the smooth look on jumpers.

Casting off   Finishing your piece of knitting.

Increasing   Making your row of knitting wider.

Decreasing   Making your row of knitting narrower.

Yarn   The wool you knit with.

Pattern   The instructions for how to make a scarf, jumper or even a pair of woolly socks.

Strange But True

◎ The World's Biggest
Knitted Christmas Tree raised nearly
£7000 for the North Devon Hospice.
Over 700 knitters helped to knit the tree,
using 1400 knitting needles and roughly
6000 balls of wool.

◎ There is an international speed-knitting
championship for the world's fastest knitters.

◎ The Tate Gallery and the Victoria and Albert
Museum in London have both staged
popular knitting events.

◎ The world's biggest knitting needles
are three metres long!

◎ National knitting week takes place
every October. Find out more at:
www.nationalknittingweek.co.uk.

Jokes

A woman is driving her car and knitting
at the same time. A police officer spots her
and yells out of her car window, "Pull over!"
"No," yells back the woman. "It's a pair of socks!"

Knitting Quiz

1 Is the author Jane West a good knitter?

2 Did Queen Elizabeth I invent knitting?

3 Is Fair Isle knitting colourful?

4 Does 'casting off' mean using your knitting needles to fish?

5 Do men in the UK like knitting?

6 Does a pair of three metre-long knitting needles exist?

Answers

1 No! But she did make a scarf once.
2 No. But she wore stockings knitted from silk.
3 Yes!
4 No. It's when you finish a piece of knitting.
5 Yes, lots. Nearly half a million men in the UK like knitting.
6 Yes. You'd need a big ball of wool to use them!

How did you score?

0–1 Oh dear. It's (k)not looking good!

2–3 Not bad. But can you tell your 'plain' from your 'purl'?

4–6 You're a knitting natural!

47

Magic Mates

RISING ★ STARS

Magic Mates books are available from most booksellers.

For mail order information
please call Rising Stars on 0871 47 23 010
or visit www.risingstars-uk.com